High-Frequency READERS™

Can You See It?

Written by Cori M. Murray
Illustrated by Karen Schmidt

Scholastic Inc.
New York   Toronto   London   Auckland   Sydney
Mexico City   New Delhi   Hong Kong

ISBN 0-439-13989-9

1 10 9 8

Printed in China

5/0
62

First Scholastic clubs printing, November 1999

Can you see it?
I see a rooster.

Can you see it?
I see a pig.

3

Can you see it?
I see a dog.

Can you see it?
I see a horse.

Can you see it?
I see a mouse.

Can you see it?
I see a skunk.

We see animals!